Dinosaur
Coloring & Activity Book

Bendon Publishing International, Inc.
Ashland, OH 44805
www.bendonpub.com

HOW MANY WORDS?

Make as many words as you can from
the word or words below.

TROPICAL RAINFOREST

_____   _____

_____   _____

_____   _____

_____   _____

_____   _____

DINO WORD SCRAMBLE

Unscramble the words below.

eqatuor

_____

suarniod

_____

extcnit

_____

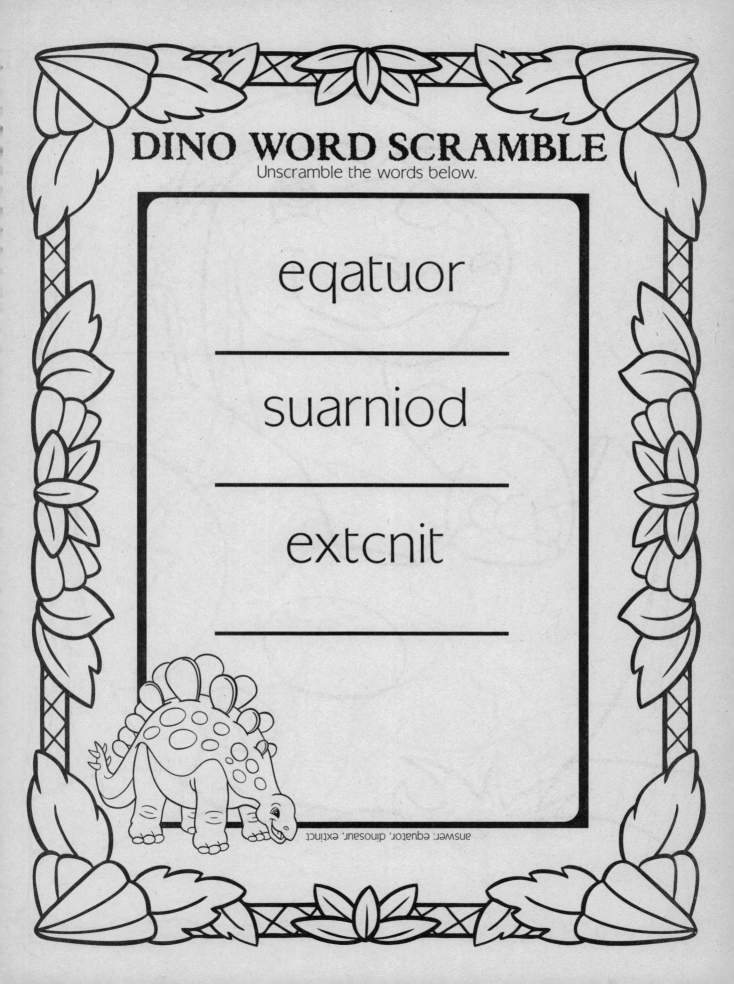

DINO SQUARES

Taking turns, connect a line from one footprint to another. Whoever makes the line that completes a box puts their initials inside the box. The person with the most squares at the end of the game wins!

example

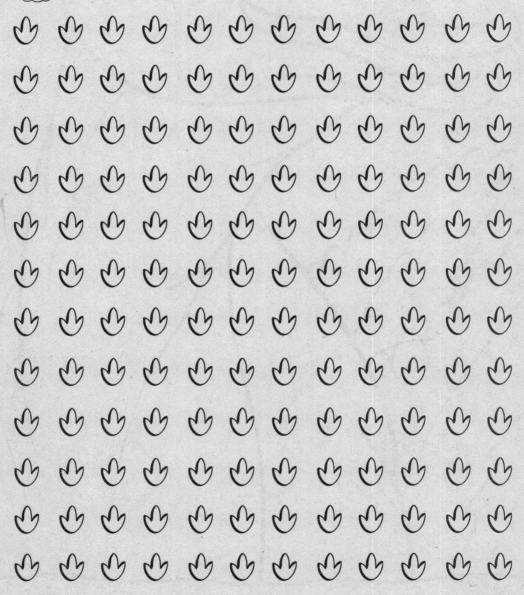

DINO TIC-TAC-TOE

The object of Tic-Tac-Toe is to get three in a row. You play on a three by three game board. The first player is known as X and the second is O. Players alternate placing Xs and Os on the game board until either opponent has three in a row or all nine squares are filled. X always goes first, and in the event that no one has three in a row, the stalemate is called a cat game.

example

HOW MANY WORDS?

Make as many words as you can from
the word or words below.

HERBIVORE DINOSAUR

_____   _____

_____   _____

_____   _____

_____   _____

_____   _____

DINO WORD SCRAMBLE

Unscramble the words below.

sisslfo

_____

iprntmis

_____

skltonee

_____

Have FUN DRAWING!

Draw and color your favorite dinosaur!

DINO WORD SCRAMBLE

Unscramble the words below.

hrebiorev

_____

cranivroe

_____

lnda

_____

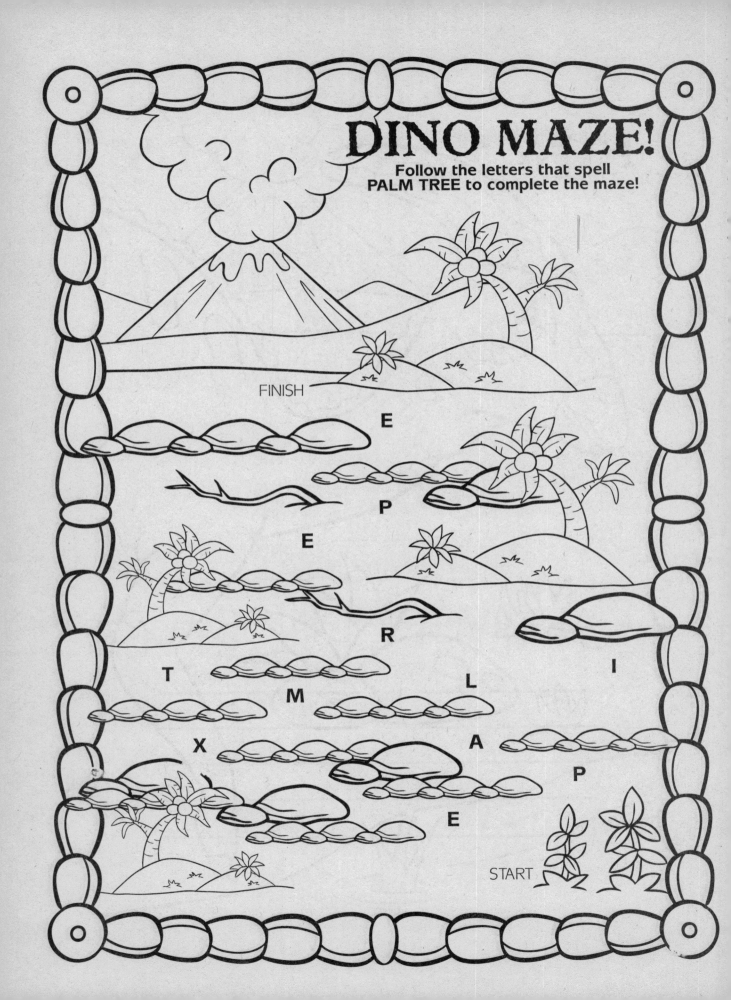

DINO MAZE!

**Follow the letters that spell
PALM TREE to complete the maze!**

FINISH

START

HOW MANY WORDS?

Make as many words as you can from
the word or words below.

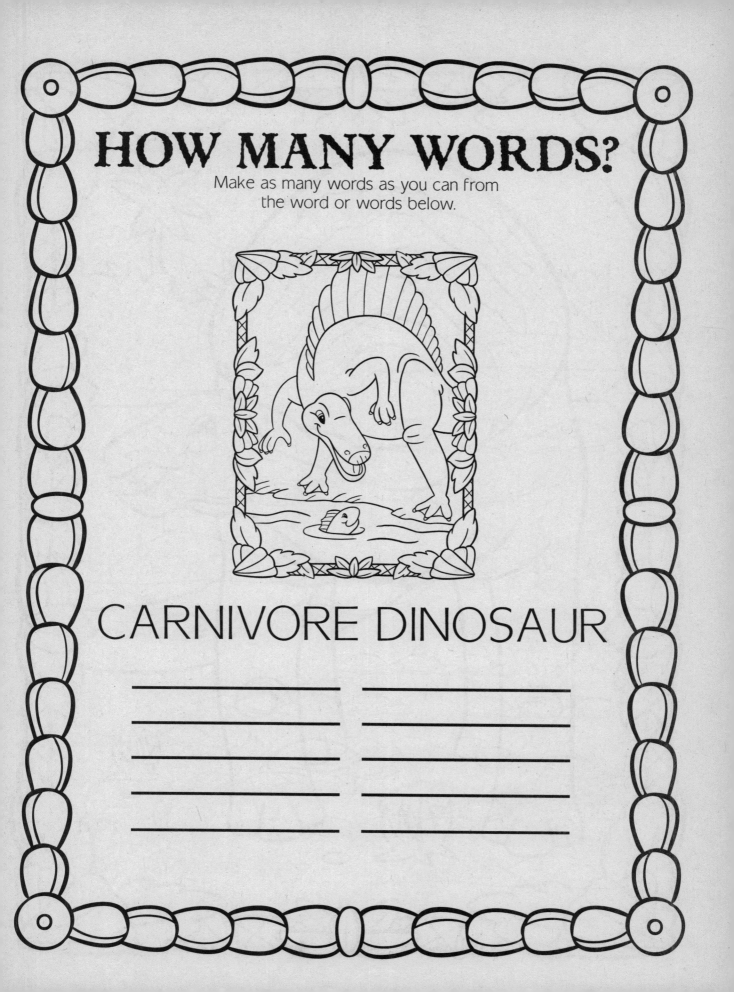

CARNIVORE DINOSAUR

_____   _____

_____   _____

_____   _____

_____   _____

_____   _____

DINO SQUARES

Taking turns, connect a line from one footprint to another. Whoever makes the line that completes a box puts their initials inside the box. The person with the most squares at the end of the game wins!

example

DINO WORD SCRAMBLE

Unscramble the words below.

nevironment

_____

gsge

_____

rpetleis

_____

DINO TIC-TAC-TOE

The object of Tic-Tac-Toe is to get three in a row. You play on a three by three game board. The first player is known as X and the second is O. Players alternate placing Xs and Os on the game board until either opponent has three in a row or all nine squares are filled. X always goes first, and in the event that no one has three in a row, the stalemate is called a cat game.

example

DINO MAZE!

Follow the letters that spell FOSSILS to complete the maze!

START

F

O
T

P   S

S

A

S

L   I

E

X   S

S

FINISH

HOW MANY WORDS?

Make as many words as you can from
the word or words below.

TRICERATOPS

_____   _____

_____   _____

_____   _____

_____   _____

_____   _____

DINO MAZE!

HELP the dinosaur find his friend by completing the maze!

START

FINISH

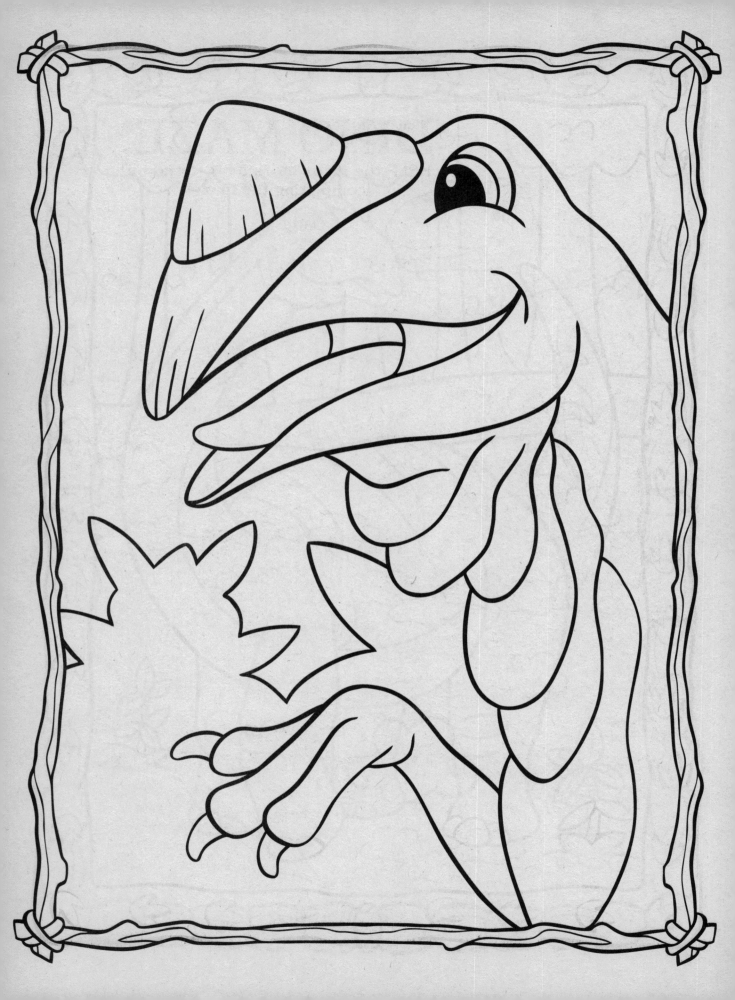

HOW MANY WORDS?

Make as many words as you can from
the word or words below.

EXTINCT SPECIES

_____   _____

_____   _____

_____   _____

_____   _____

_____   _____

DINO WORD SCRAMBLE

Unscramble the words below.

clwa

_____

nesbo

_____

clesas

_____

answer: claw, bones, scales

DINO SECRET CODE

Use the code below to fill in the blanks and reveal the fun fact about dinosaurs!

Learn a fun fact about the Velociraptor!

___ ___ ___ ___ ___ ___ ___ ___
2. 5. 10. 14. 8. 6. 10. 20.

40 ___ ___ ___ !
4. 15. 13.

1.	2.	3.	4.	5.	6.	7.	8.	9.	10.	11.
A	C	F	M	O	R	B	D	E	U	V

12.	13.	14.	15.	16.	17.	18.	19.	20.	21.	22.
G	H	L	P	I	J	K	S	N	Q	T

23.	24.	25.	26.
W	Y	X	Z

DINO TIC-TAC-TOE

The object of Tic-Tac-Toe is to get three in a row. You play on a three by three game board. The first player is known as X and the second is O. Players alternate placing Xs and Os on the game board until either opponent has three in a row or all nine squares are filled. X always goes first, and in the event that no one has three in a row, the stalemate is called a cat game.

example

Have FUN DRAWING!

Draw and color a dinosaur of your very own!
Be creative and have fun drawing!

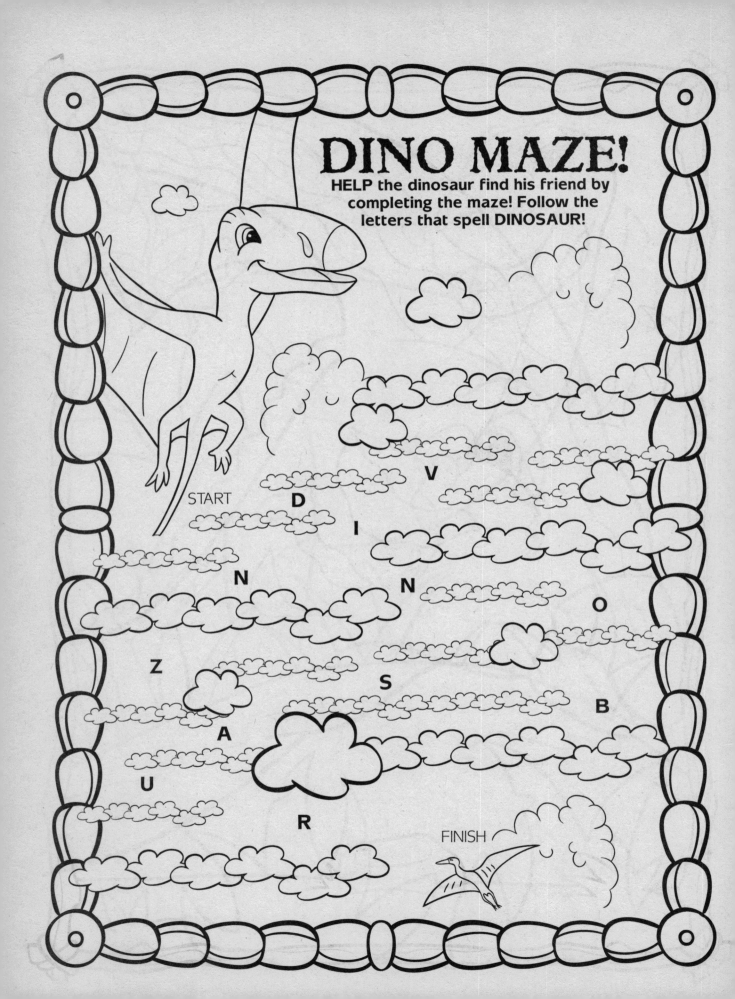

DINO MAZE!

HELP the dinosaur find his friend by completing the maze! Follow the letters that spell **DINOSAUR!**

START

V

D

I

N

N

O

Z

S

B

A

U

R

FINISH

HOW MANY WORDS?

Make as many words as you can from
the word or words below.

SCALES AND HORNS

_____   _____

_____   _____

_____   _____

_____   _____

_____   _____

Have FUN DRAWING!

Draw and color a dinosaur footprint!

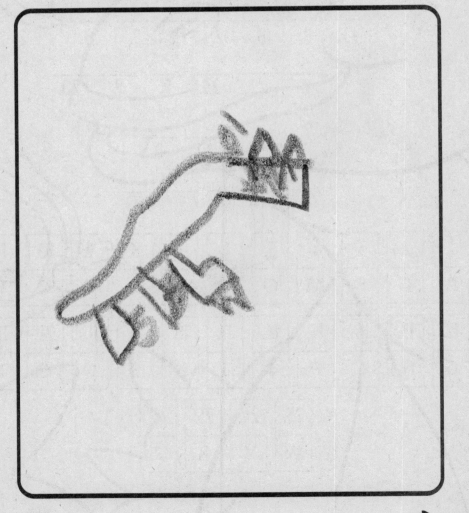

DINO SECRET CODE

Use the code below to fill in the blanks and reveal the fun fact about dinosaurs!

Learn a fun fact about the Tyrannosaurus Rex!

___ ___ ___ ___ ___ ___ ___
23. 9. 16. 12. 13. 9. 8.

___ ___ ___ ___ ___ ___ ___
7. 9. 22. 23. 9. 9. 20.

5 ___ ___ ___ **7**
    1. 20. 8.

___ ___ ___ ___
22. 5. 20. 19.

1.	2.	3.	4.	5.	6.	7.	8.	9.	10.	11.
A	C	F	M	O	R	B	D	E	U	V

12.	13.	14.	15.	16.	17.	18.	19.	20.	21.	22.
G	H	L	P	I	J	K	S	N	Q	T

23.	24.	25.	26.
W	Y	X	Z

DINO WORD SCRAMBLE

Unscramble the words below.

toofrintps

_____

tpoicalr

_____

trewa

_____

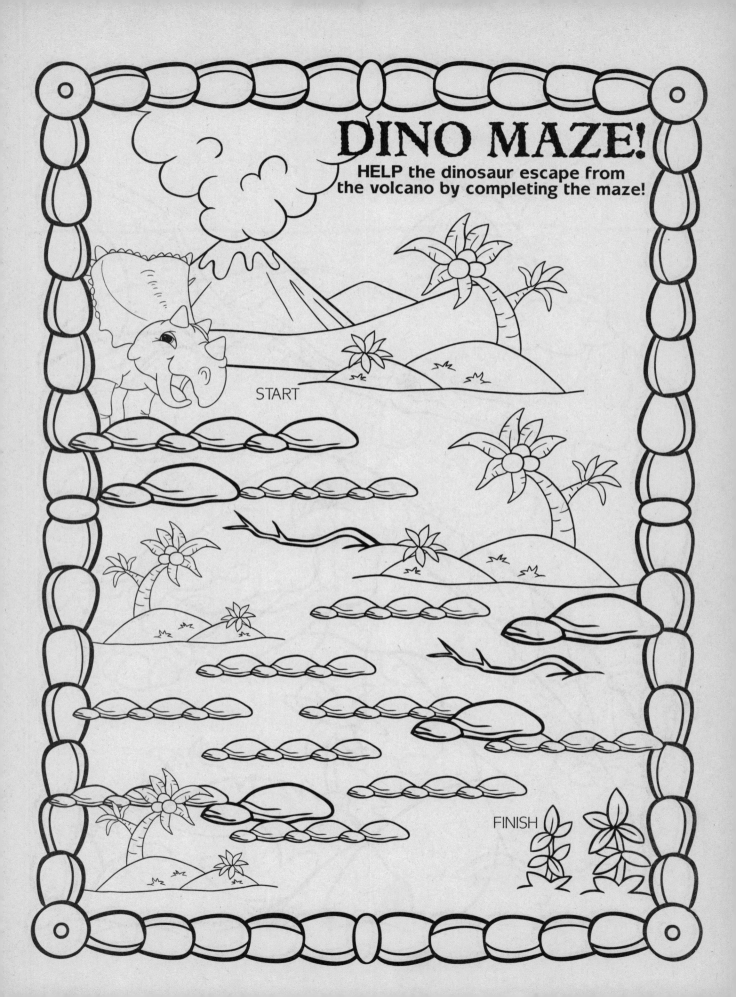

DINO WORD SCRAMBLE

Unscramble the words below.

spciese

_____

musmue

_____

syk

_____

DINO SECRET CODE

Use the code below to fill in the blanks and reveal the fun fact about dinosaurs!

Learn a fun fact about the Parasaurolophus!

___ ___ ___ ___ ___ ___ ___
22. 13. 9. 24. 1. 22. 9.

___ ___ ___ ___ ___ ___ ___ ___ ___ ___ ___
15. 16. 20. 9. 20. 9. 9. 8. 14. 9. 19.

___ ___ ___ ___ ___ ___
14. 9. 1. 11. 9. 19.

___ ___ ___ ___ ___ ___ ___ ___
1. 20. 8. 22. 23. 16. 12. 19.

1.	2.	3.	4.	5.	6.	7.	8.	9.	10.	11.
A	C	F	M	O	R	B	D	E	U	V

12.	13.	14.	15.	16.	17.	18.	19.	20.	21.	22.
G	H	L	P	I	J	K	S	N	Q	T

23.	24.	25.	26.
W	Y	X	Z

DINO SQUARES

Taking turns, connect a line from one footprint to another. Whoever makes the line that completes a box puts their initials inside the box. The person with the most squares at the end of the game wins!

example

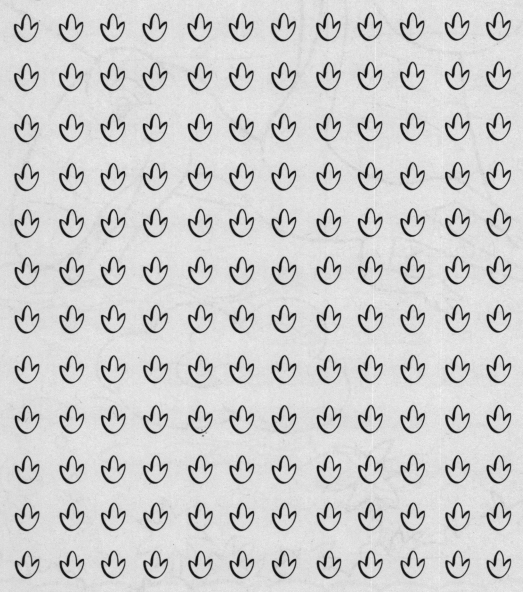

DINO MAZE!

Follow the letters that spell EXTINCT to complete the maze!

FINISH

START

Have FUN DRAWING!

Draw and color a dinosaur egg!

DINO WORD SCRAMBLE

Unscramble the words below.

hedr

____

nshor

____

lgyeoog

____

answer: herd, horns, geology

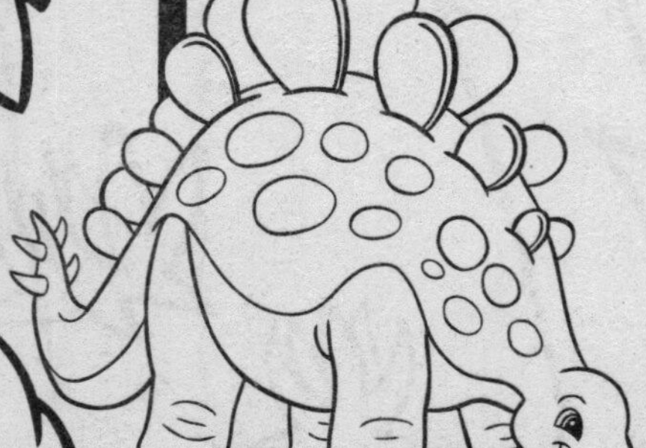

Have FUN DRAWING!

Draw and color a big volcano!

DINO SECRET CODE

Use the code below to fill in the blanks and reveal the fun fact about dinosaurs!

Learn a fun fact about the Stegosaurus!

___ ___ ___ ___ ___ ___ ___ ___ ___
13.   1.   8.   1.   7.   6.   1. 16. 20.

___ ___ ___ ___ ___ ___ ___
22. 13.   9. 19. 16. 26.   9.

___ ___ ___
5.   3.   1.

___ ___ ___ ___ ___ ___
23.   1. 14. 20. 10. 22.

1.	2.	3.	4.	5.	6.	7.	8.	9.	10.	11.
A	C	F	M	O	R	B	D	E	U	V

12.	13.	14.	15.	16.	17.	18.	19.	20.	21.	22.
G	H	L	P	I	J	K	S	N	Q	T

23.	24.	25.	26.
W	Y	X	Z

DINO SQUARES

Taking turns, connect a line from one footprint to another. Whoever makes the line that completes a box puts their initials inside the box. The person with the most squares at the end of the game wins!

example

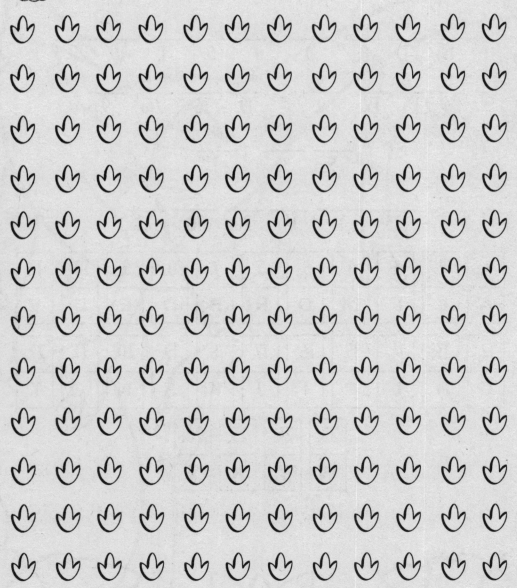

DINO SECRET CODE

Use the code below to fill in the blanks and
reveal the fun fact about dinosaurs!

**Learn a fun fact about
the Triceratops!**

___ ___ ___ ___ ___ ___ ___ ___
10. 19. 9. 13. 5. 6. 20. 19.

___ ___ ___
3. 5. 6.

___ ___ ___ ___ ___ ___ ___ ___ ___ ___
15. 6. 5. 22. 9. 2. 22. 16. 5. 20.

1.	2.	3.	4.	5.	6.	7.	8.	9.	10.	11.
A	C	F	M	O	R	B	D	E	U	V

12.	13.	14.	15.	16.	17.	18.	19.	20.	21.	22.
G	H	L	P	I	J	K	S	N	Q	T

23.	24.	25.	26.
W	Y	X	Z